MW00901208

Let's Fly This Plane!

3D Augmented Reality Scene Included

Look for this image:

> SCAN This
> Page Only for
> 3D AR Scene.

- Go to www.tutusandcars.com
- Click on the STEM Books Tab for more directions to view 3D AR scene in this book.

Tutus & Cars

tutusandcars.com

Copyright © 2021 Amaka Amalu

All rights reserved.

Email: info@tutusandcars.com

Dedication

To all the girls who haven't found their voice.
To all the girls who have.
To all the boys who support them.

FIZZZ......Emma throws a paper airplane across the room.

It flops straight to the ground.

Womp, Womp, Womp.

"Well, that was a drag," she says and sees Aunty Amaka standing in the doorway.

Emma knows her aunt is an engineer and can help solve her problem.

"How come my plane won't fly? What's wrong with it?"

"Well," says her aunt, "you have to design your plane to resist the drag from the air or wind. Think about how hard it is to run in the wind!"

"Yes, it can really push me around," Emma agrees.

"And you must design it to overcome gravity, too. You know…that pesky little thing that makes everything fall to the ground," Aunty adds with a smile.

"Come on, let's head outside. " Emma follows her aunt out the door and around to the garage.

GIANT 3D PRINTER

Aunty Amaka sits down and opens a laptop program.

"Today, we're aerospace and mechanical engineers. We'll design a plane on the computer and 3D print it."

Emma sits next to her aunt. "Seriously? Okay, let's do that!"

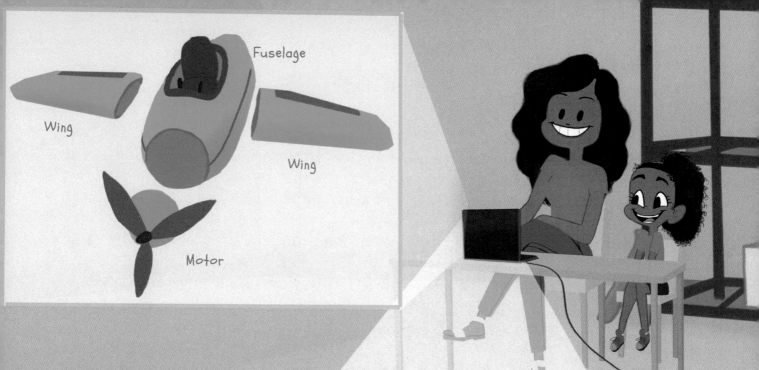

Wing

Fuselage

Wing

Motor

"So, we need to design a plane that fits you but is shaped in a way to cut through the wind drag," Aunty begins.

"Aerospace engineers design the fuselage, the body of the plane."

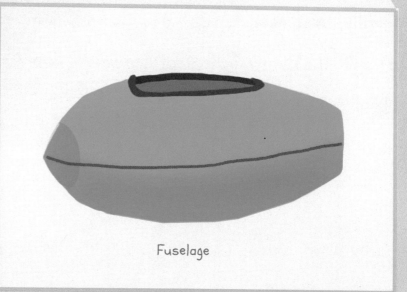

Fuselage

"They also design the wings to cut through the wind. See," she points, "the shape of the wing is very important because it causes the fast-moving air to flow over and under the wind. The high pressure air below the wing will lift up your plane into the sky."

Emma's eyes are glued to the computer screen, impressed with her Aunt's design.

"Finally, you need a fast and powerful motor that will help you lift off! That's a mechanical engineer's job to design," Aunty Amaka adds.

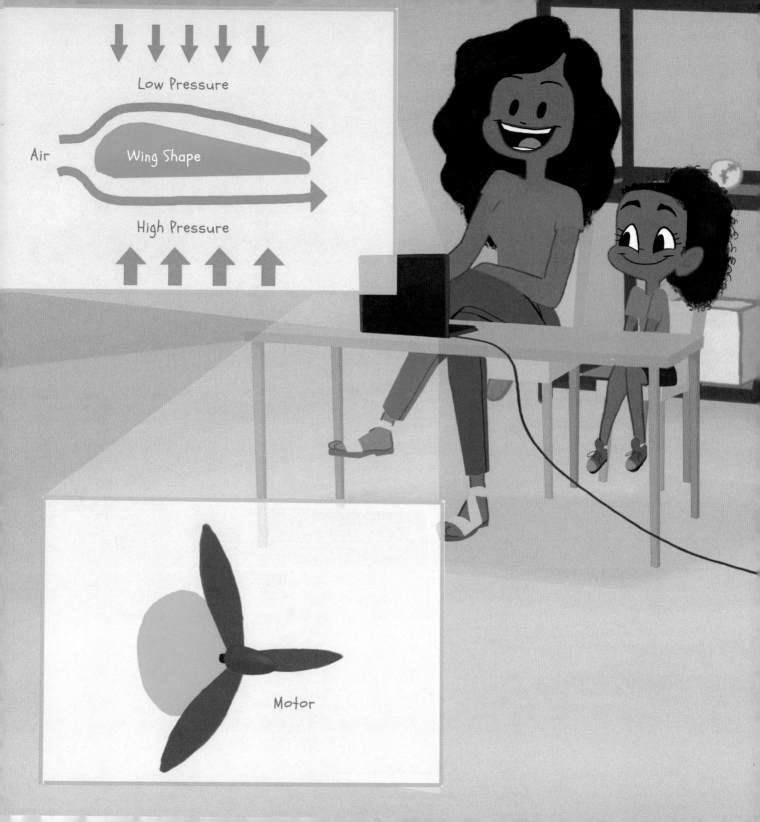

"And we're done! Go ahead and press the PRINT button, Emma!"

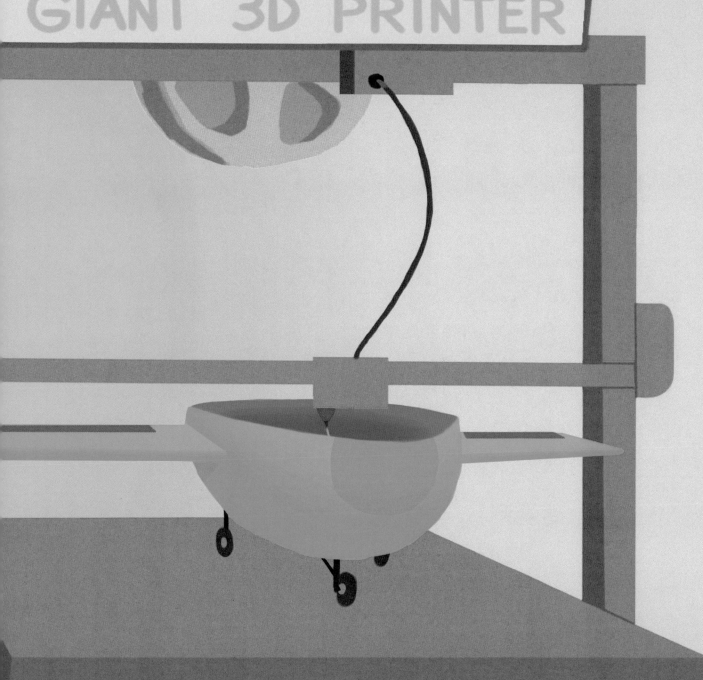

"And now," exclaims Aunty as she turns to check her laptop "this motor will thrust your plane forward at a really high speed, and your plane body shape will resist drag from the wind."

While Aunty Amaka has her back turned, Emma climbs into the plane.

"Then the fast-moving air under your wings will lift up your plane and resist gravity," Aunty continues. "And up you'll go," Aunty assures.

Emma presses on the go button, and the plane begins to move forward!

"Wooooo!!!" Emma exclaims, as her plane lifts off into the air.

Aunty Amaka looks on in shock.

SCAN This Page Only for 3D AR Scene.

What do you think happens to Emma?

Does she crash into a tall tree?

Does she have a secret parachute to jump from the plane?

Is Emma so super-smart that she lands the plane all by herself?

Nope. Aunty Amaka had thought ahead and programmed a remote control for the plane. And she soon brings Emma back safely to the ground.

Emma grins sheepishly as Aunty Amaka stares in disbelief.

"He, he. Thanks for solving my problem!" says Emma.

"When can I go back up?"

The End

Visit
TutusandCars.com
for a Paper Airplanes STEM Workshop.
Build your own paper airplane and test fly it!

Made in United States
Orlando, FL
24 August 2022

21488176R00020